The Pied Piper plays music. Everyone around him has to dance when he plays.

The Pied Piper

The witches are horrible. They work for Rumpelstiltskin.

Rumpelstiltskin is very bad. No one likes him. He wants to be King of Far Far Away.

Rumpelstiltskin

The witches

Donkey

Before you read ...
What do you know about the people on this page?

New Words

What do these new words mean?
Ask your teacher or use your dictionary.

castle

The **castle** was very old.

be born

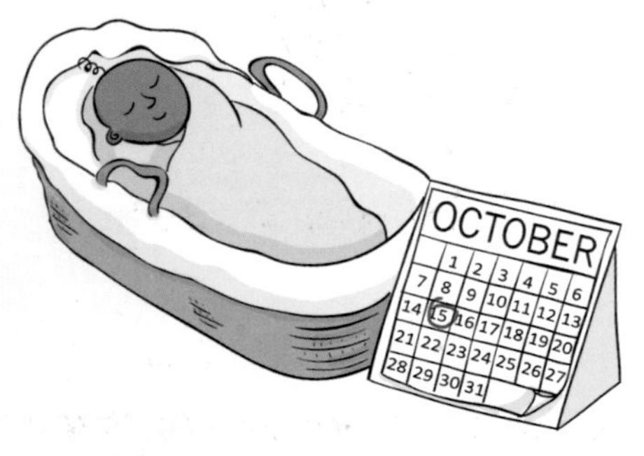

The baby **was born** on the 15th of October.

contract

'I'm buying a house. I have to put my name on the **contract**.'

carriage

The Queen has a **carriage**.

leader

The teacher is the **leader** of the class.

Level 3
High Beginner

DreamWorks

Shrek Forever After™

Meet ... everyone from

Shrek and **Princess Fiona** are ogres. They have three children.

The **King** and **Queen** of Far Far Away are Fiona's father and mother.

King

Queen

Shrek

Princess Fiona

Puss In Boots

Puss In Boots and **Donkey** are Shrek's friends.

party

The children played games at the **party**.

reward

The boy found the man's bag. The man gave a **reward** of £10 to the boy.

poster

Katie put the animal **poster** in her bedroom.

tower

The **tower** was very tall.

prison

They put the bad man in **prison**.

'True Love's Kiss'

Shrek loves Fiona very much. Fiona loves Shrek. Shrek gives **True Love's Kiss** to Fiona.

Verbs

Present	**Past**
take	took
lose	lost
fall	fell

What does the title *Shrek Forever After* mean?

Ask your teacher.

CHAPTER ONE

Beautiful in the day, ogre at night!

A long time ago, the King and Queen of Far Far Away had a baby girl.

Princess Fiona was a princess in the day, but at night she was an ogre!

'This is a big problem,' said the King.

Fiona needed True Love's Kiss.

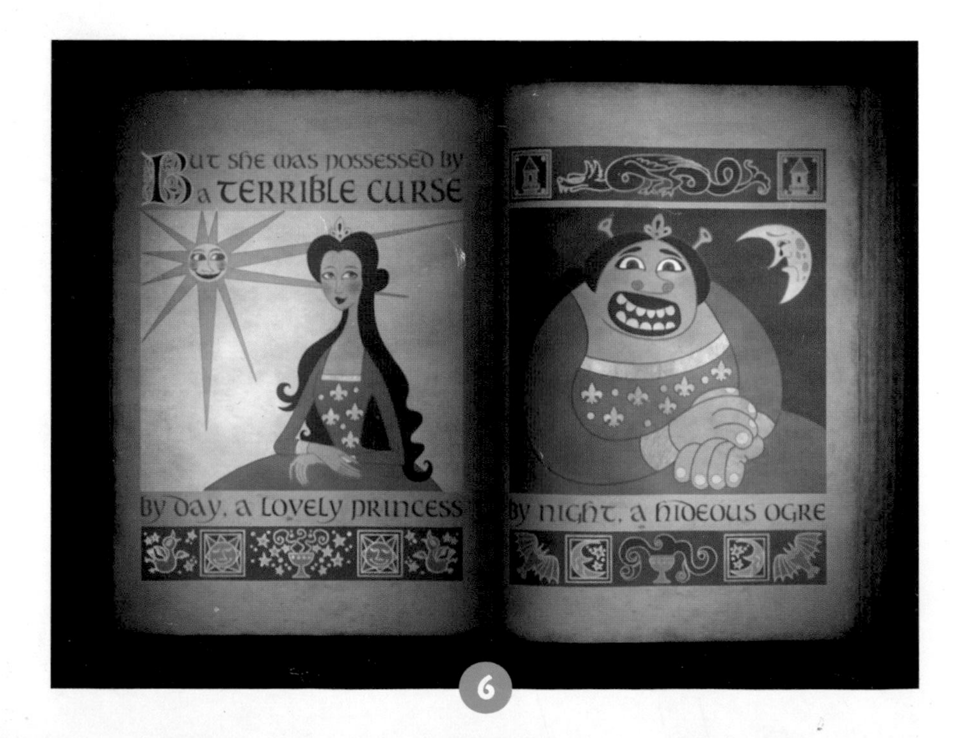

The King and Queen put Fiona in a tower. She waited and waited for True Love's Kiss.

Rumpelstiltskin came to see the King and Queen. Rumpelstiltskin was a bad man.

'I can help you,' he said. 'Fiona can be a princess all the time. But I must have Far Far Away.'

Then a man came from Fiona's tower. 'Fiona had True Love's Kiss!' he said.

Rumpelstiltskin was very angry! 'Who kissed her?' he thought.

It was Shrek. Fiona was now an ogre all the time. Shrek and Fiona were happy! Then they had children. They played with them every day.

But for Shrek it wasn't always easy. Every day was the same.

'I'm not the same Shrek now,' he thought sadly.

CHAPTER TWO
The old Shrek

Shrek and Fiona had a party for their children. All their friends were there.

'Shout like an ogre!' someone said to Shrek. But Shrek didn't shout because he was sad.

'No!' he said angrily and he went outside.

Shrek saw Rumpelstiltskin there. 'Go away!' said Shrek.

'But I can help you,' said Rumpelstiltskin.

'How can you do that?' asked Shrek.

'I can give one day of old Shrek back to you,' said Rumpelstiltskin.

'A day of old Shrek? But how?' said Shrek.

'You must give one day of your life to me.'

'Which day?'

'What about a day when you were a baby?'

'OK, you can take one day.'

'Put your name on this contract,' said Rumpelstiltskin.

Shrek did it.

Shrek walked down the road. Everyone ran away.

'Good! I'm the old Shrek again!' he thought.

CHAPTER THREE
No friends for Shrek?

Shrek saw a poster. *Wanted. Ogres. Reward!* it said.

Then he saw a 'Wanted' poster of Fiona!

'Fiona?' he thought.

Suddenly, some witches found Shrek. 'Come with us, ogre!' they shouted.

They put Shrek in a horrible carriage. He didn't like it.

'Someone's singing!' thought Shrek. Then he saw Donkey at the front of the carriage.

'Donkey!' said Shrek happily. 'Old friend!'

'Who are you?' asked Donkey.

'It's me, Shrek,' said Shrek.

'I don't know you,' said Donkey.

'But we're friends!' said Shrek.

'Donkeys and ogres can't be friends!' said Donkey.

The carriage went to the castle. Rumpelstiltskin lived there with the witches.

'Where are the King and Queen?' Shrek asked Rumpelstiltskin.

'They're not here. Everything is mine, Shrek!' said Rumpelstiltskin.

'But I don't understand,' said Shrek.

'Ha! You were never born. I took that day from you. No one knows you. Fiona never kissed you!' laughed Rumpelstiltskin.

'Oh no!' shouted Shrek. 'What did I do?'

He ran away and took Donkey with him.

'Oh Donkey, I did a terrible thing,' said Shrek. 'I put my name on Rumpelstiltskin's contract and everything is horrible now.'

Shrek started to cry.

Donkey was very sad about Shrek. He read the contract.

'Wait! We can stop the contract,' Donkey shouted happily. 'Kiss Fiona by twelve o'clock tonight. Then everything is the same as before.'

'Donkey, you are a good friend!' said Shrek. 'I must find Fiona quickly.'

CHAPTER FOUR
Where is Fiona?

Shrek and Donkey looked for Fiona. They found one hundred ogres!

'Hello,' said one ogre. 'We fight Rumpelstiltskin. Do you want to help?'

Suddenly Shrek saw Fiona. She was the leader of the ogres and Puss In Boots was her friend.

'Fiona!' shouted Shrek.

'Who are you?' she asked angrily.

'It's me! Shrek! We have beautiful ogre children.'

'I don't know you,' she said.

'I want Shrek!' shouted Rumpelstiltskin to the witches. 'He must NOT kiss Fiona.'

'Who can help me?' Rumpelstiltskin thought.

'I know!' he shouted. 'Find the Pied Piper!'

Fiona talked to the ogres. 'Every night the witches look for ogres. Tonight Rumpelstiltskin is coming with them. I want to find him!'

The ogres waited for Rumpelstiltskin and the witches.

Shrek talked to Fiona. 'Fiona, I know you.'

'How?' she asked.

'I know everything about you. I know that you sing beautifully. I know that you were in a tower. Do you want True Love's Kiss, Fiona?' said Shrek.

'No!' said Fiona.

Suddenly, Rumpelstiltskin's carriage was there. The Pied Piper came out. And the Pied Piper played. All the ogres started dancing!

Shrek, Fiona, Puss In Boots and Donkey ran away and fell into some water. The ogres danced to the castle with the Pied Piper.

Fiona and Shrek got out of the water.

'One kiss, Fiona ...' said Shrek.

Fiona kissed Shrek but everything was the same.

'Oh no!' said Shrek. 'It's because she doesn't love me,' he thought.

'I must help the ogres,' said Fiona and she started walking to the castle.

Shrek watched Fiona sadly.

CHAPTER FIVE
'Bring me Shrek!'

Rumpelstiltskin was angry. Now he had Fiona and all of the ogres. They were in prison, but Shrek wasn't!

'Bring me Shrek and you can have anything!' he shouted.

He put posters everywhere. The posters said: *Reward for Shrek*. Shrek saw a poster.

'I've got an idea,' he said.

Shrek went into the castle.

'Here I am! Now I want my reward,' said Shrek to Rumpelstiltskin.

'Only True Love's Kiss can stop our contract,' said Rumpelstiltskin.

'I'm not here to stop our contract,' said Shrek. 'I want the ogres out of prison.'

'OK,' said Rumpelstiltskin, 'but you are going to prison'.

'OK,' said Shrek sadly. He wanted Fiona out of prison.

But, of course, Rumpelstiltskin didn't do it. When Shrek came in, Fiona was in the prison too.

'Oh, Fiona, no!' Shrek said sadly.

'Rumpelstiltskin!' shouted Shrek. 'Why is Fiona here?'

'Fiona is a princess in the day. Ha!' laughed Rumpelstiltskin.

'Aaaarrrr!' Shrek shouted angrily.

'Oh Shrek!' said Fiona. 'Maybe I'm starting to love him,' she thought.

Shrek and Fiona were with Rumpelstiltskin. They were very frightened.

'Watch!' said Rumpelstiltskin to the witches. 'Dragon is going to eat Fiona! And at twelve o'clock tonight, Shrek is not going to be here! Then Far Far Away is all mine!'

Dragon came in. She was angry and hungry.

Suddenly, Donkey, Puss In Boots and the ogres came in.

'We're here, Shrek!' shouted Donkey.

The ogres jumped onto the witches.

Shrek and Fiona jumped onto Rumpelstiltskin.

'Quick, Donkey, kiss Dragon,' shouted Shrek.

Quickly, Donkey kissed Dragon. Dragon was happy.

Fiona kissed Shrek and ...

True Love's Kiss stopped the contract!

Shrek was back at the children's party again with Fiona.

'Are you OK?' Fiona asked him.

'I'm a very happy ogre!' said Shrek.

THE END

Real World

FAIRY TALE VILLAINS

In fairy tales, there is always a villain. In *Shrek Forever After*, it is Rumpelstiltskin. Here are four of the worst fairy tale villains.

Rumpelstiltskin

How old is he?

Rumpelstiltskin was first in a book in 1812. He's two hundred years old!

Why is he a villain?

He tricks people. He helps them but then he wants something from them.

What happens in the story?

Rumpelstiltskin helps a young woman but wants her first child.

The woman has a baby but she doesn't want to give the baby to Rumpelstiltskin.

'OK,' says Rumpelstiltskin. 'Say my name and you can have your child.'

The girl doesn't know his name. But, one night, she hears Rumpelstiltskin. He is singing: 'Rumpelstiltskin is my name!' Rumpelstiltskin comes for the child. But the woman says, 'You're Rumpelstiltskin!'

Rumpelstiltskin goes away. He is very angry!

★ **Which other fairy tale villains do you know? Write a list.** ★

The Queen from Snow White

The Queen was very bad! 'Snow White is NOT more beautiful than me. She must go!' she said.

The Ugly Sisters from Cinderella

The Ugly Sisters were horrible! They didn't like Cinderella. 'You can't be with Prince Charming!' they shouted.

The wolf from Little Red Riding Hood

The wolf tricked Little Red Riding Hood. He wanted to eat her!

What do these words mean? Find out.

fairy tale   villain   trick   ugly   wolf

After you read

1 Answer the questions. Circle the correct answer.

a) Who did Shrek hear singing?
Puss In Boots **Donkey**

b) Who did Shrek see on a 'Wanted' poster?
Fiona **Rumpelstiltskin**

c) Who helped Rumpelstiltskin? **the witches** **the ogres**

d) Who did Rumpelstiltskin put in prison?
Puss In Boots **Shrek**

e) Who gave True Love's Kiss? **Puss In Boots** **Shrek**

f) Who had a party? **Rumpelstiltskin** **the children**

2 Match the descriptions to the names.

a) Puss In Boots	i) They have a party
b) the witches	ii) They help Rumpelstiltskin to find Shrek.
c) Donkey	iii) He was at the front of a carriage.
d) Shrek's children	iv) He was with Fiona and the ogres.
e) the Queen	v) He gives Shrek a contract.
f) Rumpelstiltskin	vi) She is Fiona's mother.

Where's the popcorn?
Look in your book. Can you find it?

Puzzle time!

1a Complete the puzzle with the missing consonants.

1) He asked Shrek to put his name on a contract. (14)
2) They worked for Rumpelstiltskin. (7)
3) When he plays, people dance. (4, 5)
4) Shrek and Fiona were at a party for their ____. (8)
5) Fiona loved this ogre. (5)
6) Shrek kissed this ogre. (5)
7) They jumped onto the witches. (5)
8) The witches put Shrek in this. (8)
9) Shrek saw a 'Wanted ____.' (6)
10) Shrek had to give this by midnight. (13)
11) Fiona's mother (5)
12) Donkey's wife (6)

		1 R	U	M	P	E	L	S	T	I	L	T	S	K	I	N
				2	I				E							
3	I	E			I		E									
		4		I				E								
				5			E									
								6	I	O		A				
								7 O			E					
					8	A			I	A		E				
				9	O			E								
		10		U	E		O		E			I				
						11	U	E	E							
							12		A		O					

b Write the name of the film.

.... After

2 Order the sentences.

a) Shrek is back with his children again. ☐

b) Shrek wants to be old Shrek. 3

c) Fiona and Shrek have three children. 2

d) Fiona doesn't know Shrek. 4

e) Rumpelstiltskin talks to the King and Queen. 1

f) Rumpelstiltskin brings Pied Piper in. ☐

g) Rumpelstiltskin brings Dragon in. ☐

3a Who are they? Draw 'Wanted' posters. Look at page 12 to help you.

She has a baby girl called Fiona.

He talks and talks and talks!

He wears long boots and likes milk!

b Now make a 'Wanted' poster for you! Draw your face and describe who you are.

Imagine ...

Be the Pied Piper! Make some musical instruments with things around you!

a) Work in groups of four. Each person chooses one of these 'instruments'.

Drum: use your hands on a desk / chair

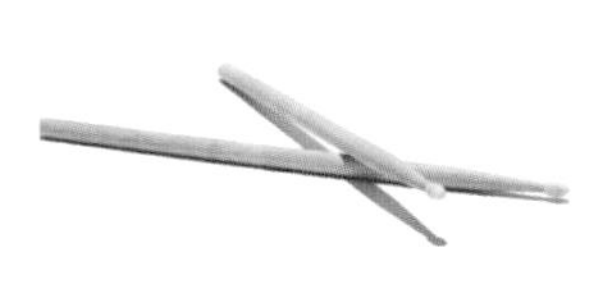

Drumsticks: hit two pens or pencils on each other

Maracas: shake a pencil-case

b) One of you is the 'Pied Piper'. The rest of the group are the dancers. Take turns.

Donkey   Fiona   ogres   Puss In Boots   Shrek   witches

Pied Piper: Choose a word from the box above.
The dancers have to say it.
Play a rhythm for one minute. It can be fast or slow!
Dancers: Dance to the rhythm. Say the word from the story.

Chant

1 Listen and read.

Shrek Forever!

In Shrek Forever After,
Shrek was very angry.
He walked away from the
party.
He wanted just one day.

In Shrek Forever After,
Rumpelstiltskin was bad.
He said, 'Shrek – why are
you sad?'
He laughed, 'Here is your day!'

In Shrek Forever After,
Fiona was a leader.
She said, 'We're going to fight
To win Far Far Away.'

In Shrek Forever After,
Fiona was in prison.
Shrek went to help her,
And Donkey too.

In Shrek Forever After,
Shrek and Fiona kissed!
They were back at the party,
And everyone was happy!

Shrek Forever After!
Shrek Forever After!
Ever after! Ever after!

2 Say the chant.